PIANO ★ VOCAL ★ GUITAR

The Big Book *of* Piano Songs

Exclusive Distributors:
Music Sales Limited
8/9 Frith Street, London W1D 3JB, England.
Music Sales Pty Limited
120 Rothschild Avenue, Rosebery, NSW 2018, Australia.

Order No. HLE90002440
ISBN 1-84609-094-6
This book © Copyright 2005 by Hal Leonard Europe

Cover design by Chloë Alexander
Printed in the USA

Your Guarantee of Quality
As publishers, we strive to produce every book to the highest commercial standards.
The book has been carefully designed to minimise awkward page turns and to make playing from it a real pleasure.
Throughout, the printing and binding have been planned to ensure a sturdy, attractive publication
which should give years of enjoyment.
If your copy fails to meet our high standards, please inform us and we will gladly replace it.

www.musicsales.com

This publication is not authorised for sale in the
United States of America and/or Canada.

Hal Leonard Europe
Distributed by Music Sales

ALONE

Words and Music by BILLY STEINBERG
and TOM KELLY

Recorded a half step lower.

BEAUTIFUL

Words and Music by
LINDA PERRY

Moderately slow

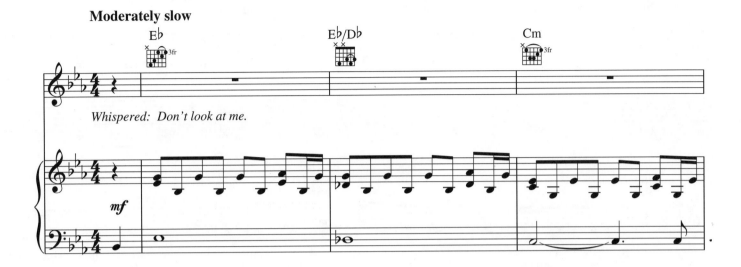

Whispered: *Don't look at me.*

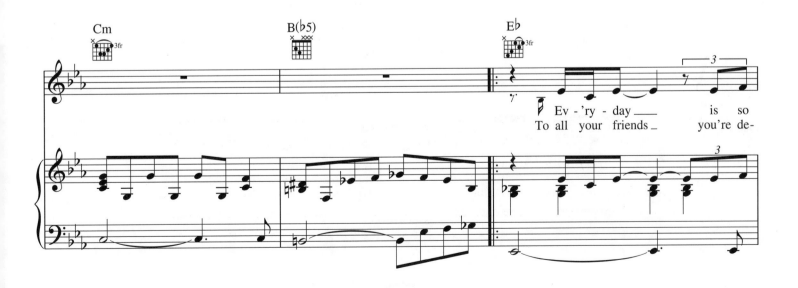

Ev -'ry - day ___ is so
To all your friends ___ you're de-

ANGEL

Words and Music by
SARAH McLACHLAN

Original key: D♭ major. This edition has been transposed down one half-step to be more playable.

BENNIE AND THE JETS

Words and Music by ELTON JOHN
and BERNIE TAUPIN

Slowly, deliberately

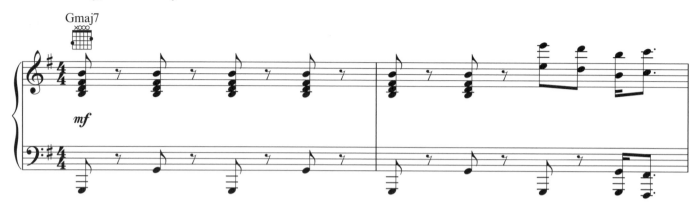

Hey, kids, __ shake __ it loose to - geth - er. The spot - light's hit - ting some - thing that's been known to change the weath - er.
Hey, kids, __ plug __ in - to the faith - less. May - be they're __ blind - ed, but Ben - nie makes them age - less.
Solo ad lib.

BRICK

Words and Music by BEN FOLDS
and DARREN JESSEE

CANDLE IN THE WIND

Music by ELTON JOHN
Words by BERNIE TAUPIN

CRAZY

Words and Music by
WILLIE NELSON

CLOCKS

Words and Music by GUY BERRYMAN, JON BUCKLAND,
WILL CHAMPION and CHRIS MARTIN

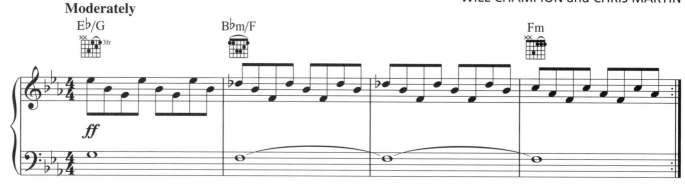

Lights go out and I can't be saved. __ Tides that I tried to
Con - fu - sion __ nev - er stops. __ Clos - ing __ walls and

swim a - gainst __ brought me down up - on my knees. __
tick - ing clocks __ gon - na come back and take you home. __ I

And noth - ing else com - pares.

D.S. al Coda
(with repeats)

(They Long to Be)
CLOSE TO YOU

Lyric by HAL DAVID
Music by BURT BACHARACH

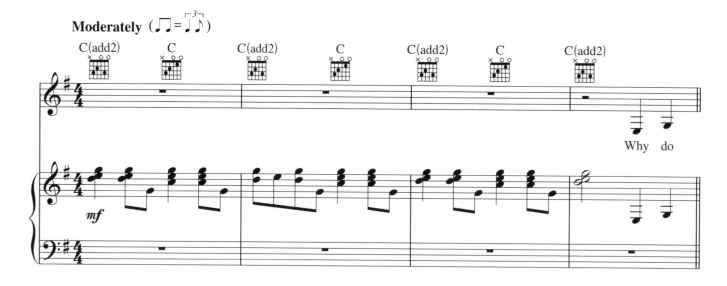

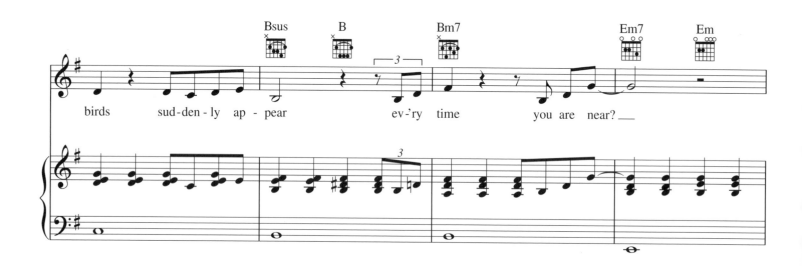

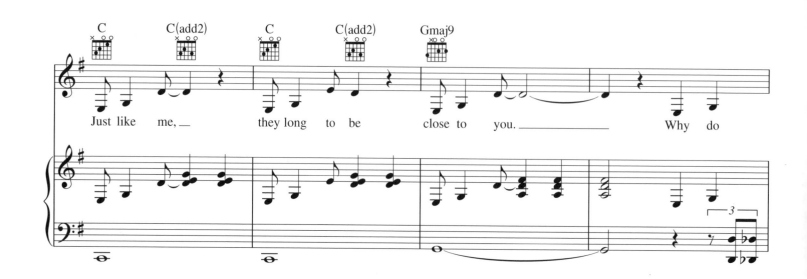

COME SAIL AWAY

Words and Music by
DENNIS DeYOUNG

COULD IT BE MAGIC

Inspired by "Prelude in C Minor" by F. Chopin

Words and Music by BARRY MANILOW
and ADRIENNE ANDERSON

DON'T KNOW MUCH

Words and Music by BARRY MANN,
CYNTHIA WEIL and TOM SNOW

DON'T KNOW WHY

Words and Music by
JESSE HARRIS

DON'T LET THE SUN GO DOWN ON ME

Words and Music by ELTON JOHN
and BERNIE TAUPIN

DON'T LOOK BACK IN ANGER

Words and Music by
NOEL GALLAGHER

Verse 2:
Take me to the place where you go
Where nobody knows if it's night or day
Please don't put your life in the hands
Of a rock 'n' roll band who'll throw it all away.

I'm gonna start a revolution from my head
'Cause you said the brains I had went to my head
Step outside, the summertime's in bloom
Stand up beside the fireplace, take that look from off your face
'Cause you ain't never gonna burn my heart out.

EVERYBODY'S CHANGING

Words and Music by TIM RICE-OXLEY,
RICHARD HUGHES and TOM CHAPLIN

(Everything I Do)
I DO IT FOR YOU

from the Motion Picture ROBIN HOOD: PRINCE OF THIEVES

Words and Music by BRYAN ADAMS,
ROBERT JOHN LANGE and MICHAEL KAMEN

Lyrics:

Look in-to my eyes, you will see what you mean to me. Search your heart, search your soul, and when you

Look in-to your heart, you will find there's noth-ing there to hide. Take me as I am, take my life, I would

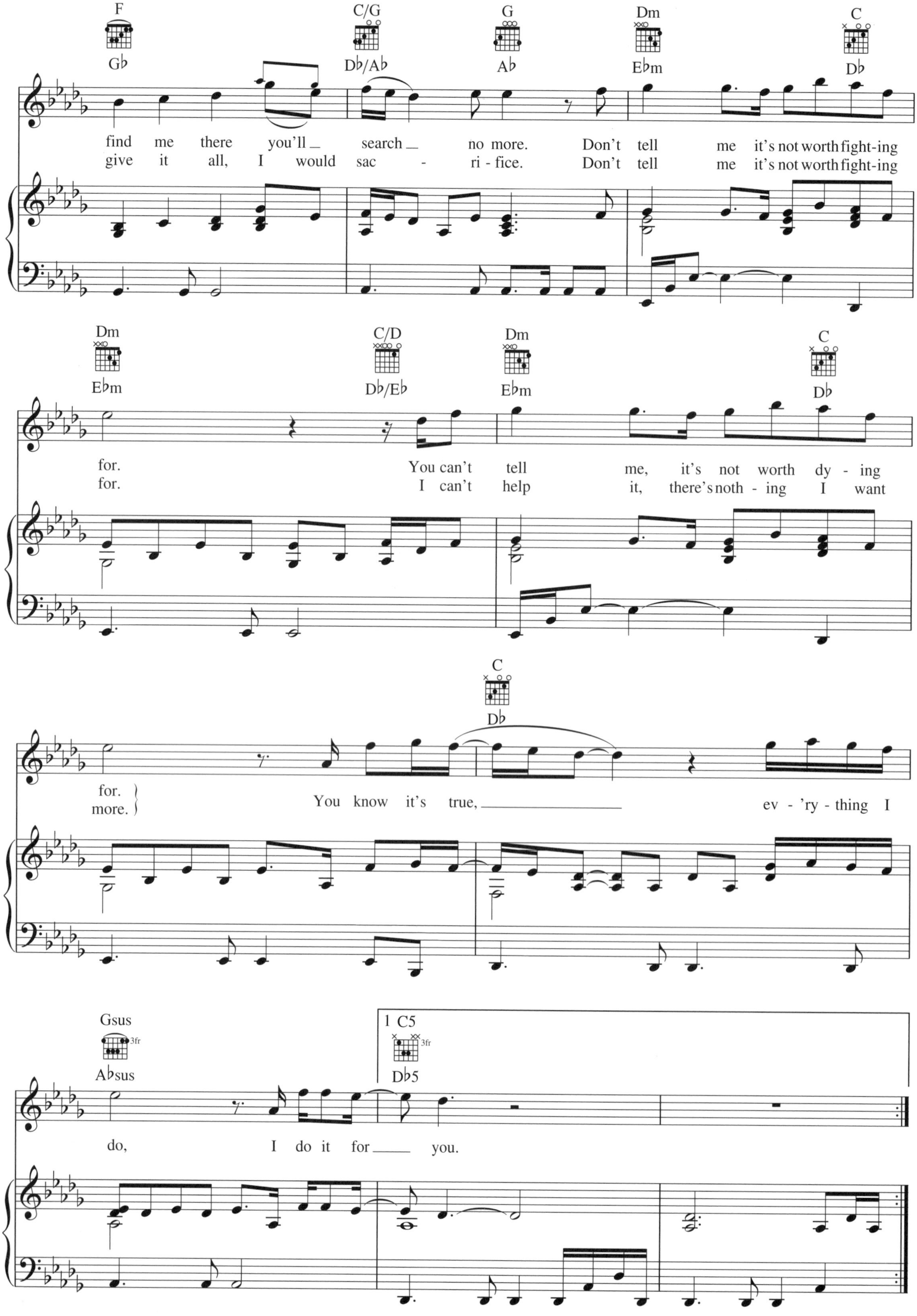

GEORGIA ON MY MIND

Words by STUART GORRELL
Music by HOAGY CARMICHAEL

GLORY OF LOVE
Theme from KARATE KID PART II

Words and Music by DAVID FOSTER,
PETER CETERA and DIANE NINI

We'll live for - ev - er, know - ing to - geth - er that we

did it all for the glo - ry of love.

Just like a knight in shin - ing ar - mor, from a long time a - go,

HAVE I TOLD YOU LATELY

Words and Music by
VAN MORRISON

Slowly, with expression

Have I told ____ you late - ly that I love you? Have I

told you there's no one else ____ a - bove ____ you?

Fill my heart ___ with glad - ness, take a - way all ____ my sad - ness,

GOODBYE YELLOW BRICK ROAD

Words and Music by ELTON JOHN
and BERNIE TAUPIN

When are you gon-na come down? When are you going to land?
What do you think you'll do then? I bet they'd shoot down the plane.

I should have stayed on the farm. I should have
It-'ll take you a cou-ple of vod-ka and ton-ics to

lis-tened to my old man. You know you can't hold me for-ev-er,
set you on your feet a-gain. May-be you'll get a re-place-

HARD TO SAY I'M SORRY

Words and Music by PETER CETERA
and DAVID FOSTER

HERO

Words and Music by MARIAH CAREY
and WALTER AFANASIEFF

HOW WILL I KNOW

Words and Music by GEORGE MERRILL,
SHANNON RUBICAM and NARADA MICHAEL WALDEN

Original key: G♭ major. This edition has been transposed up one half-step to be more playable.

* Cues 2nd time only

LET IT BE

Words and Music by JOHN LENNON
and PAUL McCARTNEY

When I find my-self in times of trou-ble
Instrumental

Moth-er Mar-y comes to me speak-ing words of wis-dom; let it

be. And in my hour of dark-ness, she is

I DON'T WANT TO WAIT

Words and Music by
PAULA COLE

I WRITE THE SONGS

Words and Music by
BRUCE JOHNSTON

JUST ONCE

Words by CYNTHIA WEIL
Music by BARRY MANN

LADY MADONNA

Words and Music by JOHN LENNON
and PAUL McCARTNEY

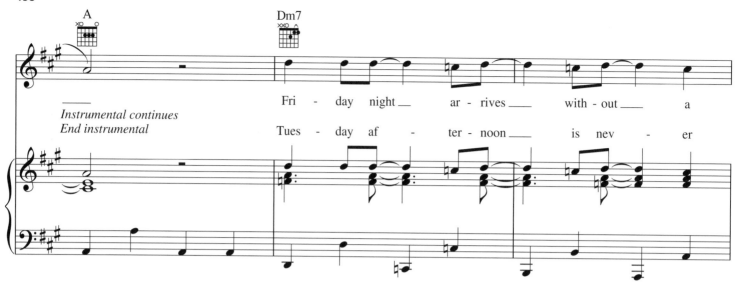

Instrumental continues
End instrumental

Fri - day night ___ ar - rives ___ with - out ___ a
Tues - day af - ter - noon ___ is nev - er

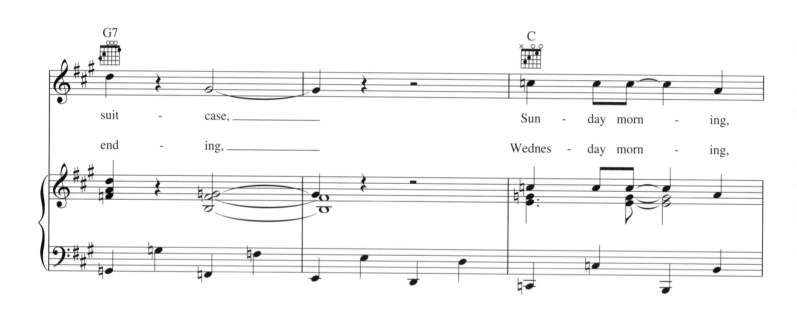

suit - case, ___ Sun - day morn - ing,
end - ing, ___ Wednes - day morn - ing,

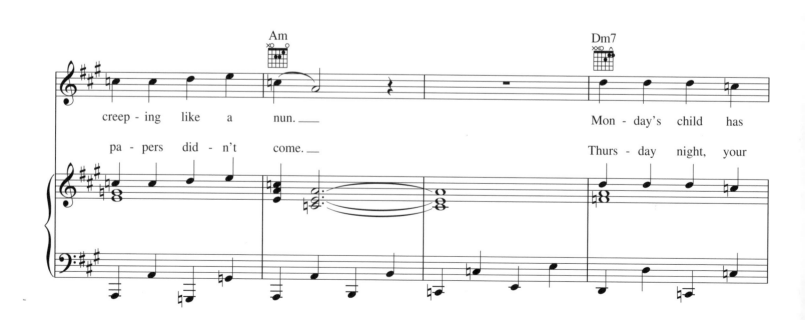

creep - ing like a nun. ___ Mon - day's child has
pa - pers did - n't come. ___ Thurs - day night, your

LOOK WHAT YOU'VE DONE

Words and Music by
NIC CESTER

Moderate Rock Ballad

Take my pho-to off the wall

___ if it just ___ won't sing for you. ___

'Cause all that's left has gone a-way ___ and there's noth - ing there ___

LOOKS LIKE WE MADE IT

Words and Music by RICHARD KERR
and WILL JENNINGS

MANDOLIN RAIN

Words and Music by B.R. HORNSBY
and JOHN HORNSBY

MORNING HAS BROKEN

Musical Arrangement by CAT STEVENS
Words by ELEANOR FARJEON

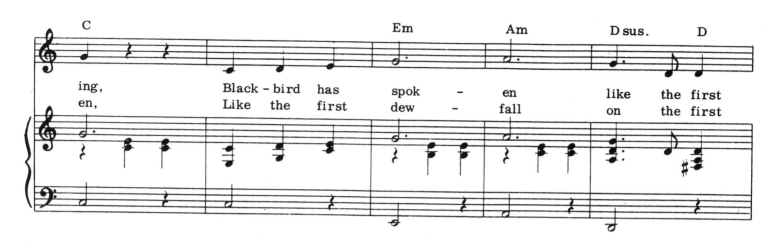

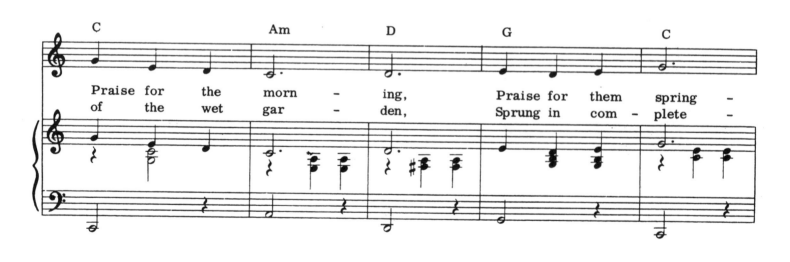

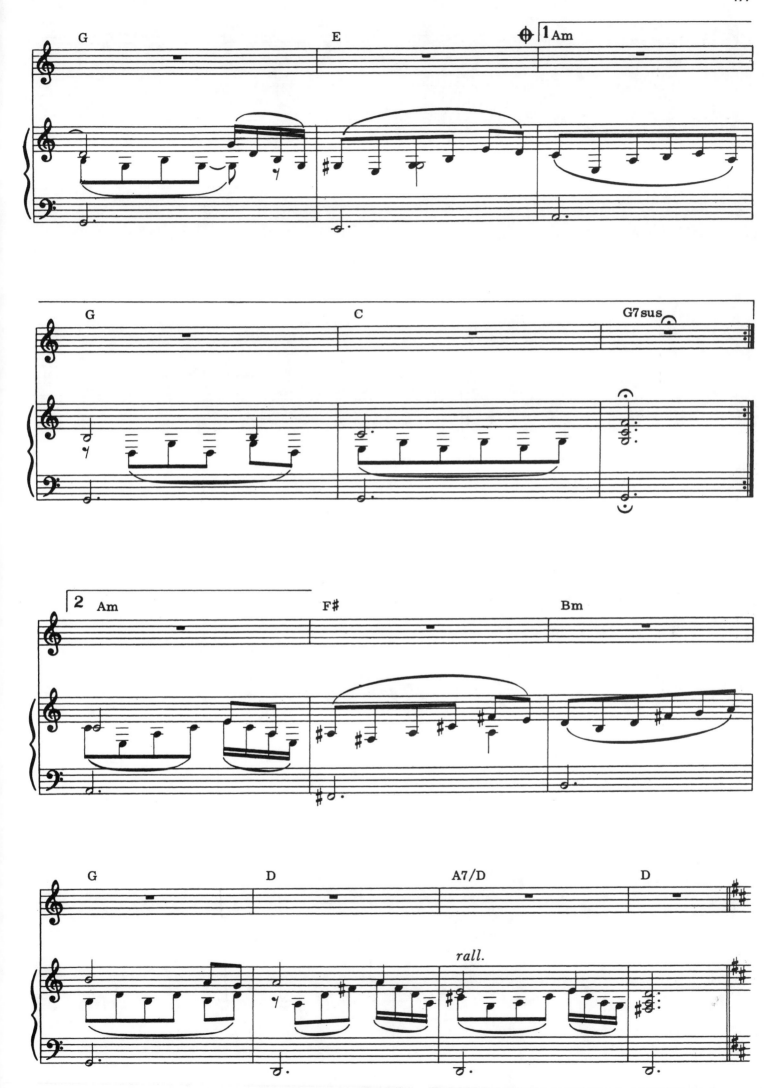

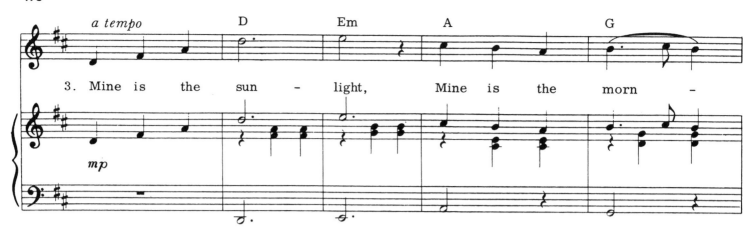

3. Mine is the sun - light, Mine is the morn -

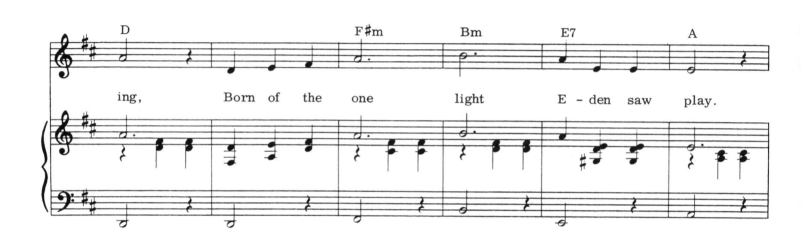

ing, Born of the one light E - den saw play.

Praise with e - la - tion, Praise ev-'ry morn -

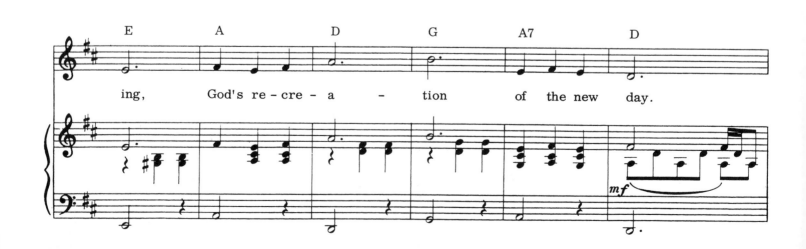

ing, God's re - cre - a - tion of the new day.

PEOPLE ARE STRANGE

Words and Music by
THE DOORS

PLEASE FORGIVE ME

Words and Music by
DAVID GRAY

Verse 2:

Help me out here, all my words are falling short
And there's so much I want to say
Want to tell you just how good it feels
When you look at me that way
Ah, when you look at me that way.

Verse 3:

Throw a stone and watch the ripples flow
Moving out across the bay
Like a stone, I fall into your eyes
Deep into that mystery
Ah, deep into some mystery.

Verse 4:

I got half a mind to scream out loud
I got half a mind to die
So I won't ever have to lose you, girl
Won't ever have to say goodbye
I won't ever have to lie
Won't ever have to say goodbye.

RUNAWAY

Words and Music by JON BON JOVI
and GEORGE KARAKOGLOU

SILLY LOVE SONGS

Words and Music by PAUL McCARTNEY
and LINDA McCARTNEY

Moderately Bright

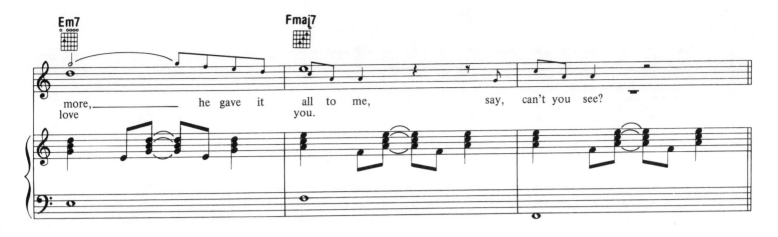

WALKING ON BROKEN GLASS

Words and Music by
ANNIE LENNOX

Walk-ing on, walk-ing on bro-ken glass. _____

You were the
Now ev-'ry

sweet-est thing _____
one of us is made to suf-fer,

that I ev-er knew, _____
ev-'ry one of us is made to weep,

STUCK IN A MOMENT YOU CAN'T GET OUT OF

Lyrics by BONO and THE EDGE
Music by U2

A THOUSAND MILES

Words and Music by
VANESSA CARLTON

Mak-ing my way _ down - town, _ walk - ing fast. _ Fac - es pass _ and I'm home - bound.

* Recorded a half step higher.

THE VALLEY ROAD

Words and Music by B.R. HORNSBY
and JOHN HORNSBY

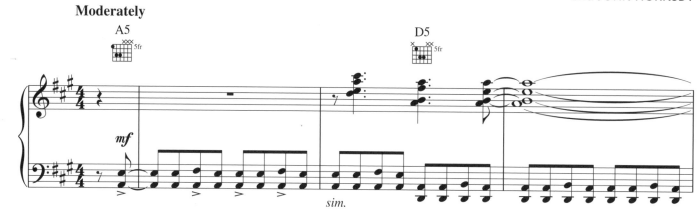

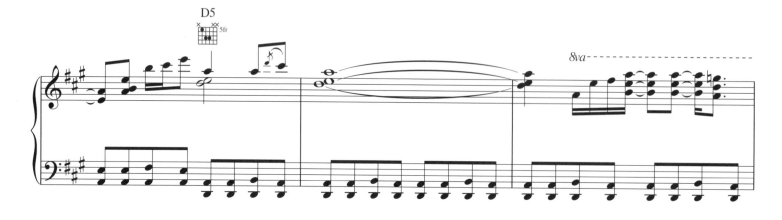

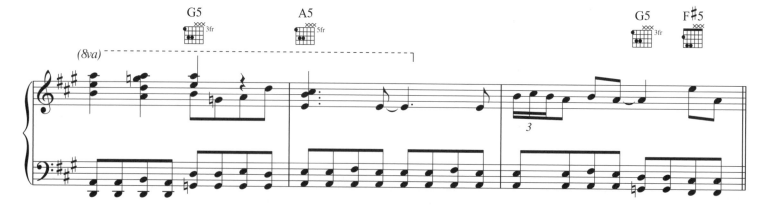

WALKING IN MEMPHIS

Words and Music by
MARC COHN

YOU ARE SO BEAUTIFUL

Words and Music by BILLY PRESTON
and BRUCE FISHER

Moderately slow, expressively

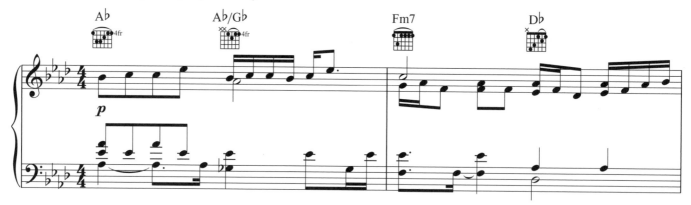

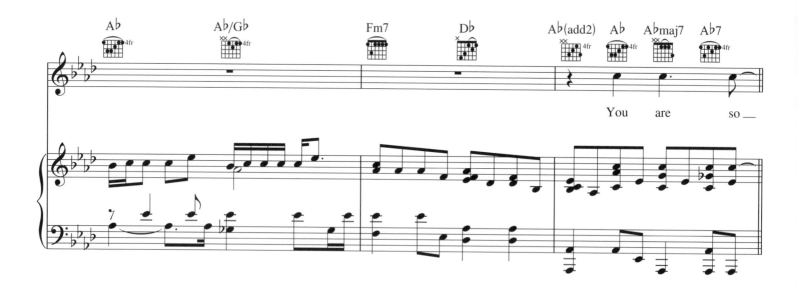

You are so ___

___ beau - ti - ful ___

to

8vb   *loco*

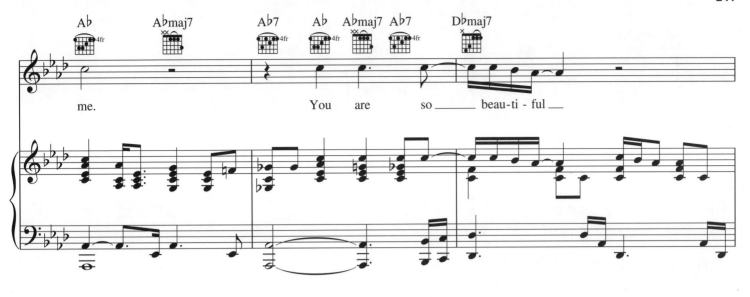

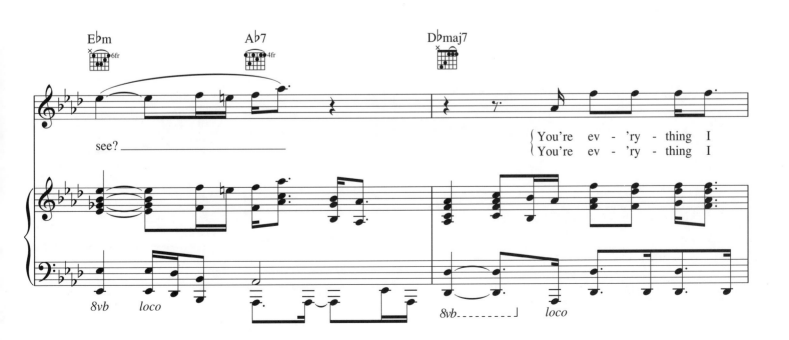

hope for.
hope for,

You're ev-'ry-thing I need. ___

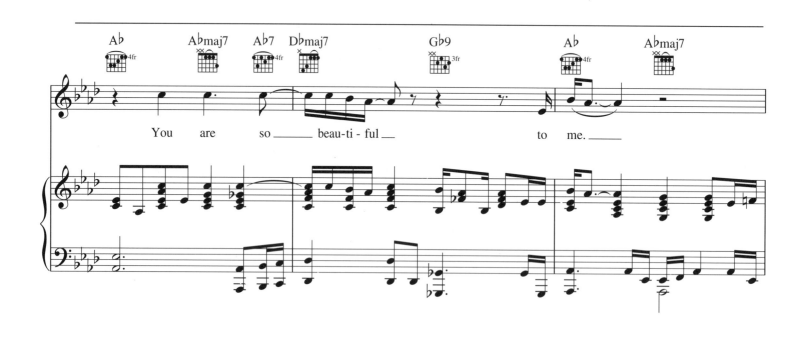

You are so ___ beau-ti-ful ___ to me. ___

You are so ___ ev-'ry-thing I need.

You are so ____ beau-ti-ful ____ to ____

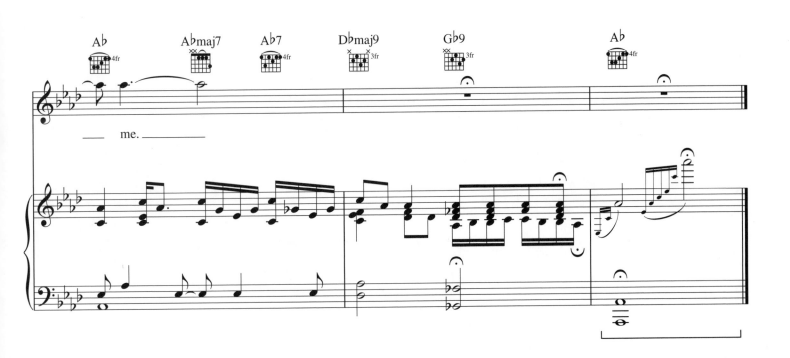

____ me. ____

YOUR SONG

Words and Music by ELTON JOHN
and BERNIE TAUPIN

Slow, but with a beat

It's a lit-tle bit fun-ny, _____ this feel-ing in-side; _____
If I was a sculp-tor, _____ but then _ a-gain, no, _____ or a

I'm not one of those _ who _ can eas-i-ly hide. _____
man who makes po - tions in a trav-el - in' show, _____ I

Don't _ have much mon-ey, _____ but, boy, if I did, _____
know _ it's not much but it's _ the best I can do. _____

YOU DO SOMETHING TO ME

Words and Music by
PAUL WELLER